HOW TO TAKE CARE OF YOUR PET

DINOSAUR

YOUR PET

VELOCIRAPTOR

By Kirsty Holmes

THE
OFFICIAL
FOSSIL
GUIDE

THE **SECRET BOOK COMPANY**

©This edition published in 2020. First published in 2019.

The Secret Book Company

King's Lynn
Norfolk PE30 4LS

ISBN: 978-1-91250-246-2

All rights reserved

Printed in Malaysia

A catalogue record for this book is available from the British Library.

Written by:
Kirsty Holmes

Edited by:
Madeline Tyler

Designed by:
Danielle Jones

All facts, statistics, web addresses and URLs in this book were verified as valid and accurate at time of writing. No responsibility for any changes to external websites or references can be accepted by either the author or publisher.

IMAGE CREDITS

Cover – solar22, Bibela, ONYXprj, stuckmotion, isaree, Kurt Natalia. 1 & throughout ~ stuckmotion, solar22. 4 – Hilch, janevision. 5 – Sentavio. 6 – HitToon. 7 – Glinskaja Olga. 9 – Spreadthesign, Iconic Bestiary, RoseRodionova. 10 – Dreamcreation. 11 – Sentavio. 12 – Dasha D. 13 – tereez, Glebova Galina. 14 – robuart. 15 – Dreamcreation, Lemberg Vector studio, MicroOne. 16 – Park Ji Sun. 17 – Mascha Tace, Mr.Thanakorn Kotpootornv. 18 – truefiesta, vectortatu. 19 – lukpedclub. 20 – Pogorelova Olga, Julia Tim, Red sun design, Elena3567. 21 – small shrimp, Leremy. 22 – Pirina, Evgenii Bobrov. 23 – vladwel, Gaynore. Images are courtesy of Shutterstock.com. With thanks to Getty Images, Thinkstock Photo and iStockphoto.

CONTENTS

PAGE 4   F.O.S.S.I.L.

PAGE 6   Eggs

PAGE 8   Babies

PAGE 10   Growth

PAGE 12   Food

PAGE 14   Exercise

PAGE 16   Naming

PAGE 18   Washing

PAGE 20   Problems

PAGE 22   Tricks

PAGE 24   Glossary and Index

THE
OFFICIAL
FOSSIL
GUIDE

Words that look like <u>this</u> can be found in the glossary on page 24.

F.O.S.S.I.L.

So, you're the proud owner of a dinosaur egg. Congratulations!

Owning a pet dinosaur is a lot of hard work, but it's worth the trouble. Dinosaurs make excellent pets.

CONGRATULATIONS! IT'S A... VELOCIRAPTOR!

Per 1
Gn +1
C6/M7
P5/E2
M1 1.3

E WITH CARE HAND
CARE HANDLE WITH

If you are a first-time dinosaur owner, you probably have lots of questions. Never fear! This handy F.O.S.S.I.L. guide will tell you all you need to know.

F.O.S.S.I.L. FACT

F.O.S.S.I.L. stands for:

Federal
Office of
Super
Sized
Interesting
Lizards

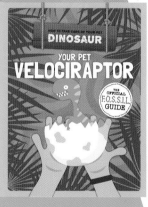

HOW TO TAKE CARE OF YOUR PET
DINOSAUR

YOUR PET
VELOCIRAPTOR

THE OFFICIAL
F.O.S.S.I.L.
GUIDE

EGGS

Velociraptor eggs are about the size of turkey eggs.

Velociraptor eggs should stay quite warm. Build a <u>nest</u> somewhere cosy, and keep your eggs covered.

YOU SHOULDN'T NEED TO SIT ON THE EGGS YOURSELF. A SCARF OR JUMPER WILL DO THE JOB NICELY.

BABIES

Your baby Velociraptor will hatch from its egg covered with <u>down</u>. Take care to keep the baby warm at first.

Velociraptor babies won't be very good at hunting straight away.
It's best to feed them a diet of minced meat until they are larger.

GROWTH

Your Velociraptor will grow into an adult quite quickly. It will keep its feathers as it grows up – it can be exciting to see what colour your pet will turn out to be!

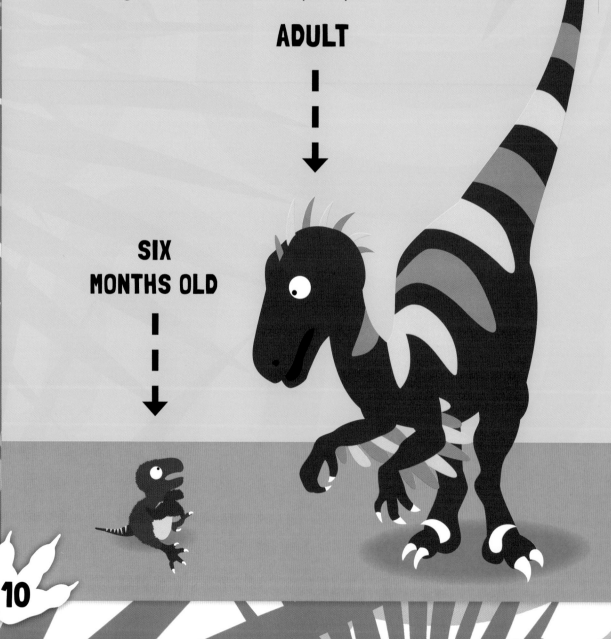

ADULT

SIX MONTHS OLD

If you were expecting a large pet, like you see on the TV, think again. Adult Velociraptors grow up to two metres long from teeth to tail. This is about the size of a large dog and means your pet can live comfortably in your house.

FOOD

Velociraptors are <u>carnivores</u>. They have up to 30 sharp teeth, perfect for tearing into a nice, juicy steak. Velociraptors are good at hunting and <u>scavenging</u>.

Velociraptors like to hunt in groups. However, you don't want your pet going after the neighbour's dog. Make sure you give your Velociraptor a toy so it can safely follow its <u>instincts</u>.

EXERCISE

Velociraptors have a top speed of about 65 kilometres per hour. When taking your pet for a walk, it is best to ask your parents to drive alongside in their car, so you can keep up.

Velociraptors can only run this fast for a short amount of time. A short run to the park will be perfect, and here you can try out your Velociraptor's other skills, such as climbing trees.

NAMING

Naming your Velociraptor is very important when <u>bonding</u> with your pet. You could choose a name that describes your pet's looks.

HOOKS

16

A Velociraptor is very fast, so you could choose a name that will let people know this.

GO, ZIPPY!

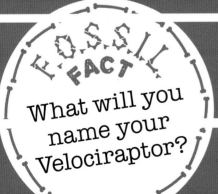

F·O·S·S·I·L FACT

What will you name your Velociraptor?

WASHING

You will not need to clean your Velociraptor very often. Feathered creatures will <u>preen</u> themselves. Some will like a bath, so provide a special bird bath in your garden for this.

Other Velociraptors might prefer a dust bath. After a bath or preen, your Velociraptor might like to sit in the sun for a while.

PROBLEMS

Your Velociraptor is an excellent hunter and will follow its instincts. Because of this, it does not get along well with other pets and should be kept alone.

Even if they like you, Velociraptors can have a bit of a temper. Learn the warning signs that your pet is in a bad mood – such as hissing – and give them space until they calm down.

SHHH...

TRICKS

Teach your Velociraptor some simple commands. If your pet learns well, give them a treat. If your pet shows natural talent, you could enter them in a pet show.

Working with your pet can be very rewarding – you might even win a prize!

THERE ARE HOURS OF FUN TO BE HAD WITH YOUR FRIENDLY NEW PET!

WINNER!

GLOSSARY

BONDING — forming a close relationship

CARNIVORES — animals that eat other animals rather than plants

DOWN — fluffy feathers covering baby birds

INSTINCTS — strong natural behaviour or abilities

NEST — any place used by an animal to lay eggs or rear young

PREEN — trim and clean feathers, like a bird does

SCAVENGING — feeding on other animals that are already dead

INDEX

BATHS 18–19

FEATHERS 10, 18

MEAT 9, 12

NESTS 7

SPEED 14, 17

TEETH 11–12